KU-334-256

Drum Strum or Tickle

Matters Medical
by
Hayden Jeffery

Foreword

I hope very much you will take this book in the way that it is intended as a means of helping even those who develop cancer to see the funny side of things. Hayden has done brilliantly well in his own fight against cancer and if you buy this book it will help him raise some money for cancer care.

He tells us his first public exhibition of doubtful artistic talent was at age 5 years. His pastel was displayed at Primary School where a clever clogs classmate noticed that his brilliant Santa Claus did not possess a beard. In defence Hayden claimed that it was tucked inside Santa's uniform jacket.

Hayden studied art at school, technical drawing then Cartographical draughtsmanship. He flew planes in the R.N then entered NHS labs, Medical Research Council, vet labs, Pharmaceuticals and later Quality Assurance, Audit & Consultancy. On retirement he continued with art as a hobby. It is his hope that this cartoon book will help in a small way to break down the "Stiff Upper Lip" surrounding cancer and the unbelievable reluctance of so many to seek early intervention and treatment.

Rev Richard Burkitt. *March 2013*

Copyright Hayden Jeffery May 2013

Printed and published by FTRR Printing and Publishing,60 Grant St Inverness IV3 8BS
fortherightreasons@rocketmail.com

ISBN 978-1-905787-37-1

This book is dedicated to my Grandmother (see right for my portrait of her). She was widowed and left to bring up six children. My Grandmother and I were very close and fully understood each other, despite her deaf- ness which limited conversation. Anyone looking for solace would certainly have bene- fited from meeting my Gran who had no ene- mies and was loved by all who met her. I detect in my portrait of her both sadness and cheerfulness. Perhaps the picture con- veys something special to those seeking sup- port and peace of mind.

"What will be, will be. There is no sense in worrying. The Lord will provide." She would say.

Hayden Jeffery

4

INTRODUCTION

THE THREE WISE MEN DIDN'T BRING ME FRANKINCENSE AND MYRRH WHEN I WAS BORN. IN FACT IT WAS DIFFICULT TO FIND THREE WISE MEN IN 1939 AND EVEN MORE DIFFICULT WHEN WORLD WAR11 BROKE OUT.

I WAS BLESSED WITH ONE DOCTOR, NURSE LEADBETTER AND MY AUNT, WITH THE "MANGER" BEING A SCOTTISH SPECIAL HOUSING ASSOCIATION TERRACED HOUSE.

I REMEMBER HAPPILY SWIMMING IN THE AMNIOTIC FLUID, PRIOR TO MY BIRTH WHEN I OVERHEARD MY MOTHER SAY (SHE WAS ALSO PRESENT), THAT DR.CAMPBELL WOULD BE AVAILABLE. KNOWING THE HISTORICAL REPUTATION OF THE CAMPBELLS, (I WAS BORN VERY KNOWLEDGEABLE BECAUSE BBC RADIO WAS ALWAYS ON) FOR BEING MORE EFFICIENT AT TAKING HUMANS OUT OF THE WORLD RATHER THAN BRINGING THEM BACK IN. I WAS ALREADY IN A STATE OF APPREHENSION AND FEAR.

I PLUCKED UP COURAGE, HOWEVER AND EVENTUALLY EMERGED HOPING THAT NURSE LEADBETTER WAS NOT A LEAD BEATER! MY WORKING CLASS ORIGINS WERE SECURELY EMPHASIZED BY MY AUNT WHO PROMPTLY PLACED THIS COLD, WET 7 POUND OF MINCE WITHIN THE ENVELOPING FOLDS OF "THE DAILY MIRROR". THE HUMILITY OF THIS ACT IS STILL WITH ME TO-DAY AT OVER 70YRS! WHEN I BUY "THE TIMES" I FEEL PANGS OF CONSCIENCE AND GUILT IN TURNING MY BACK ON MY HUMBLE ENTRY INTO THE WORLD.

LIFE IS A MIXTURE OF FUN AND WORRY AND MANY STATES IN BETWEEN. TOMORROW YOU WILL REFLECT ON YOUR CONCERNS OF TODAY WHICH PROBABLY TURN OUT TO BE OF NO CONCERN! SO WHY WORRY? REFLECT ON THESE CARTOONS OF TODAY WHICH ARE INTENDED TO BE OF NO CONCERN i.e. JUST FOR FUN

Hayden Jeffery

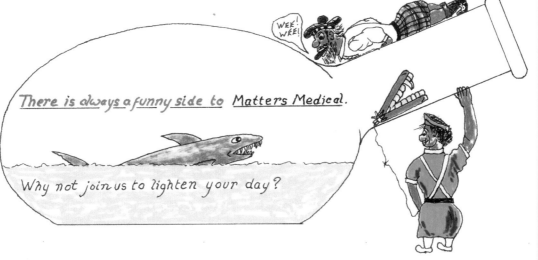

IT IS A WISE MAN WHO SEEKS EARLY DETECTION OF ANY FORM OF CANCER.

"GALILEO (1564-1642), HELP ME TO FIND CANCER!"

THE STARS HAVE NOT DEALT ME THE WORST THEY COULD DO:
MY PLEASURES ARE PLENTY, MY TROUBLES ARE TWO.
BUT OH, MY TROUBLES THEY REAVE ME OF REST
THE BRAINS IN MY HEAD AND THE HEART IN MY BREAST.
OH GRANT ME THE EASE THAT IS GRANTED SO FREE
THE BIRTHRIGHT OF MULTITUDES, GIVE IT TO ME,
THAT RELISH THEIR VICTUALS AND REST ON THEIR BED
WITH FLINT IN THE BOSOM AND GUTS IN THE HEAD.

A.E.HOUSEMAN,(1859-1936)

I'M FED UP TOO! TIRED MEDICS COME HERE FOR RELAXATION, FORGET THEY'RE ON A HORSE AND TELL US TO TO CANALIZE, CASTRATE, CANCER, CANKER AND CAPSULATE, &c., —EVERYTHING EXCEPT CANTER! THE POOR THINGS CAN'T SWITCH OFF!

A CASE OF AQUATIC NARCISSUM (FROM GREEK NARKISSOS).

A NYMPH CALLED ECHO WAS REPULSED BY THE BEAUTIFUL YOUTH CALLED NARCISSUS. SHE PINED AWAY IN GRIEF UNTIL ONLY HER VOICE REMAINED.

ARTEMIS, WHO HAD POWER TO SEND THE PLAGUE AND SUDDEN DEATH, WAS ANGERED BY NARCISSUS'S REJECTION. ARTEMIS CAUSED HIM TO FALL IN LOVE WITH HIS OWN REFLECTION IN A FOUNTAIN. IN DESPAIR NARCISSUS TOOK HIS OWN LIFE AND WAS CONVERTED INTO THE NARCISSUS FLOWER.

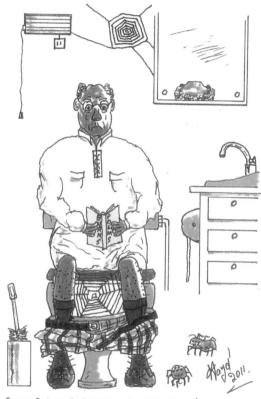

SILLY PLACE TO BUILD YOUR WEB SITE!

REMEMBER OLD ALBERT THE PIPE LAGGER. HIS NICKNAME WAS "ASBESTOS." WHEN HE DIED THEY TRIED CREMATION BUT THE FLAMES WOULDN'T TAKE.

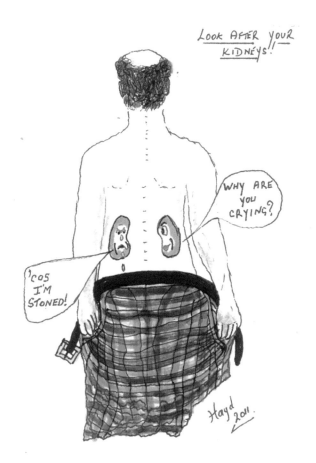

When under treatment one makes many friends. The experience of real genuine care in this often troubled world is very HUMBLING. REMEMBRANCE OF THESE TIMES AND PLACES AND THE ENCOURAGEMENT TO LOOK FORWARD TO A FUTURE FULL OF HOPE IS, BELIEVE IT OR NOT, BEST EXPRESSED IN BURNS` "AULD LANG SYNE."~

SHOULD AULD ACQUAINTANCE BE FORGOT
AND NEVER BROUGHT TO MIND?
SHOULD AULD ACQUAINTANCE BE FORGOT
AND AULD LANG SYNE.

CHORUS
FOR AULD LANG SYNE, MY JO,
FOR AULD LANG SYNE,
WE`LL TAK` A CUP O` KINDNESS YET.
FOR AULD LANG SYNE.
AND SURELY YE`LL BE YOUR PINT STOWP!
AND SURELY I'LL BE MINE!
AND WE`LL TAK A CUP O` KINDNESS YET,
FOR AULD LANG SYNE.

Lady Cackle-Berry Ward
TIMES
NOTE:-
IN BERKSHIRE AN EGG IS A CACKLE BERRY!
"TO HELL WITH HYGIENE. WHEN "MY LADY"
WANTS FRESH EGGS,– SHE GETS FRESH EGGS!"
Hayd 2013.

O world! O life! O time!
On whose last steps I climb
Trembling at that where I had stood before
When will return the Glory of your prime? P.B. SHELLEY (1792-1822)

"HIS DOCTOR TOLD HIM TO ENJOY HIS DRINK BECAUSE HE WAS TOO FAR GONE, - THAT WAS 20 YEARS AGO!" FOR EQUITY RELEASE READ ALCOHOL INCREASE.

W.Shakespeare (1564-1616), unwittingly wrote the caption for me when the advice goes wrong:

"Bring your slave, what should I do but tend upon the hours and times of your desire? I have no precious time to spend nor services to do till you require."

GOD BLESS OUR PARTNERS

QUESTION WHAT MEANS 'TO WIN'?
WHAT NOW IS DISABILITY?
YOU WON HEARTS WITHIN.
YOU INCREASED THE WORLD'S SENSIBLITY.
RESPECT IS NOW GOLD, WORLDWIDE.
(final stanza in poem entitled "The Paralympics 2012)

She was a phantom of delight
When first she Gleam'd upon my sight
A lovely apparition, sent
To be a moments Ornament
W Wordsworth (1770-1850)

Don't ever despair.
In life there is always someone
Destined for someone.

THOSE PILLS CERTAINLY CURED MY DOUBLE VISION!

Floyd 2010.

GOOD MORNING. THIS IS YOUR (EX-AIR AMBULANCE), OPERATOR SPEAKING.
WELCOME ABOARD SCANNER No. 2. MY NAME IS MR. HANS VON CANCERTROPP. WE WILL
BE SCANNING IN THREE PHASES AT 6000 WATTS FOR 30 MINUTES. ESTIMATED TIME
OF TERMINATION 10.30 HRS. PLEASE ACQUAINT YOURSELF WITH THE EMERGENCY
PROCEDURE BECAUSE I VILL BE THE FIRST TO RUN AVAY.

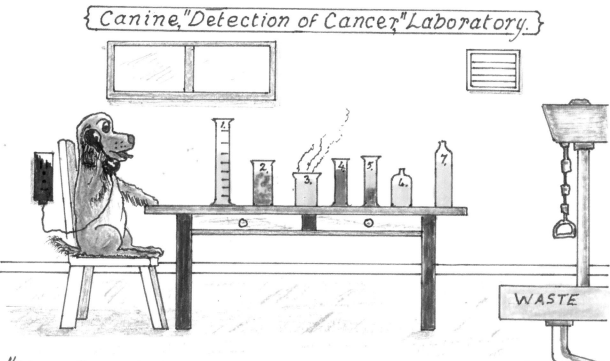

"MY MUM TOLD MY FATHER THAT
CHASING THE SUN WOULD END UP
IN MEL- AN- OMA!
IS THAT A SEASIDE RESORT ON THE MED?

DOC: NAME PLEASE?

PATIENT:~ *KAN KNOT REMEMBA*.

DOC: THAT`S A UNIQUE NAME, NICE RING TO IT!
NOW THEN, FATHERS COUNTRY OF ORIGIN?

PATIENT:~ DON`T KNOW WHERE HE CAME FROM, DON`T KNOW WHERE HE
WENT TO!   ANYWAY, WHAT`S YOUR NAME DOC?

DOC: WELL~ER~UMM, *DO KNOT REMEMBA*.

PATIENT:~ DAD!   I`VE FOUND YOU!

31

I HEARD THAT YOU HAD AN "ECO-BABY?"
YEA! I TOLD THE LAB THAT I WANTED A BABY
WITH GENES WHICH WOULD
MAKE HIM "THE LIGHT OF MY LIFE."

35

The tension between kindness, and kind deeds that are done just for show, is here today as it was 120 years ago.

"The Hospital" 1898

All things Must come to an end

Well, Folks, I have tried my best to show you my interpretation of the funny side of matters medical. Previews of the cartoons have revealed a diversity of opinions and reactions to either the cartoons or captions. Psychologically, it has been a fascinating project for a retired research scientist like myself, we are all so different in our views on life in general that it surprises me that we can finally agree on anything!

If we don't—Some fight!

Please don't take the latter action. Buy my little bookie and if you can't laugh today then there is, hopefully, always tomorrow. Many thanks to everyone who has bought my book whoever and wherever you are.

Try not to worry about too much in life, it really isn't worth it! Love your life as best you can, although this is often very difficult.

My wife has been a volunteer in Oncology and always found cancer patients very positive and cheerful. Take one day at a time and always look forward.

Regards

Hayden.